PREFACE

Students in Levels 2 and 3 will be able to enjoy these pieces. The style of music in this collection uses non-traditional harmonies. In only one piece will you find major and minor chords!

Even though the pieces may be in unfamiliar modes and whole tone scales, the same methodical way of learning should take place—look for similar or repeated patterns in each piece and give attention to dynamics, phrasing, and fingerings!

We hope you enjoy these pieces imitating various dinosaurs!

Neil A. Kjos Music Company
James Bastien
Jane Smisor Bastien

A BRIEF HISTORY OF DINOSAURS

Dinosaurs lived long ago, before humans, and roamed the earth for over 140 million years. The word dinosaur comes from two Greek words, *deinos* and *sauros* meaning terrible lizard. However, none of the dinosaurs were lizards.

There were many kinds of dinosaurs, some as small as a chicken and some giant sized. Some dinosaurs had claws, others had horns, some had "armor" plates and spiked tails to protect them. There were even duck-billed dinosaurs. Most dinosaurs laid eggs.

The age of the dinosaurs is divided into three periods: the **Triassic** (try-ASS-ik) **Period** (225-190 million years ago), the **Jurassic** (ju-RASS-ik) **Period** (190-135 million years ago), and the **Cretaceous** (kree-TAY-shuss) **Period** (100-65 million years ago).

The age of the dinosaurs ended some 65 million years ago so they are now extinct. No one knows why the creatures died. It may have been from a sudden change in the earth's temperature from very hot to very cold.

Scientists have learned much about dinosaurs from fossils (once living things) found in rocks or in limestone. Many natural history museums contain dinosaur skeletons.

ABOUT THE COMPOSER

James Bastien has written a great deal of music for both children and adults. He graduated from Southern Methodist University where he studied with Gyorgy Sandor.

Mr. Bastien has been a faculty member at Notre Dame, Tulane, and Loyola Universities, and a summer faculty member at Tanglewood and the National Music Camp at Interlochen, Michigan.

He now resides in La Jolla, California, where he and his wife continue to write music of interest to piano students.

CONTENTS

√*

*To reinforce the feeling of achievement, the teacher or student may put a √ when the page has been mastered.

ISBN 0-8497-9347-5

Plateosaurus (plat-e-o-SAWR-us) lived in the **Triassic Period**. They were larger than the Procompsognathus, about 20 feet long. These dinosaurs ran on hind legs and were mainly plant-eaters.

PLATEOSAURUS

8

In the **Jurassic Period** 150 million years ago there lived many kinds of dinosaurs. Brachiosaurus (brak-e-o-SAWR-us), nicknamed Great Arms, was the largest kind. It weighed between 50–80 tons. It had a very large body and a very small head. Because of its weight it stayed mostly in the water; the water helped support the weight. Brachiosaurus was slow-moving and awkward and did not eat meat.

BRACHIOSAURUS

Ponderously (heavily)

Brontosaurus (bront-o-SAWR-us), from the **Jurassic Period** was quite large, weighing 30–40 tons. It had a large body and a small head, and did not eat meat.

BRONTOSAURUS

Heavily

* Called a cluster. Sometimes written as

12

Allosaurus (al-lo-SAWR-us) from the **Jurassic Period**, did not eat plants; it ate meat. It was a fearsome killer that attacked other dinosaurs. Allosaurus had a large head with a big mouth and sharp teeth. It walked on its hind legs and used its claws for catching prey.

ALLOSAURUS

Fast!

Allosaurus attacks!

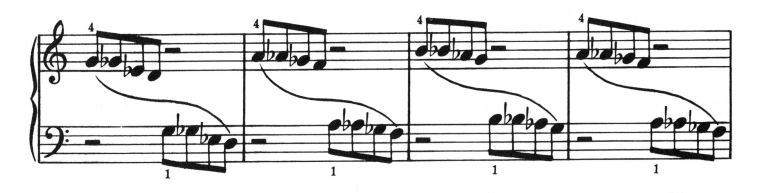

Allosaurus
catches its prey!

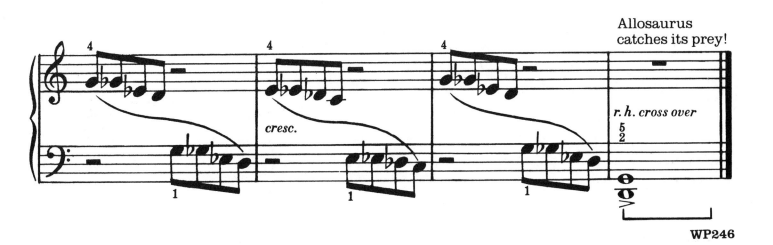

The **Cretaceous Period**, 120 million years ago, produced many kinds of armoured dinosaurs. Stegosaurus (steg-o-SAWR-us), nicknamed Covered Lizard, had armor plates standing up from its back. It had a small head and a brain about the size of a walnut. Stegosaurus stood on four feet and had four sharp spikes at the end of its tail to use in defense against enemies.

STEGOSAURUS

Triceratops (try-SER-a-tops), nicknamed Three Horn Face, was a dinosaur with a large head crowned with pointed frills. It was a large meat-eater with a pointed beak and sharp teeth. Triceratops was very powerful and mean-tempered.

TRICERATOPS

Stridently

Monoclonious (mon-o-KLON-e-us) had just one single horn on the end of its snout. The horn was long and sharp to use for self-defense.

MONOCLONIOUS

Protoceratops (prot-o-SER-a-tops), nicknamed First Horned Face, did not have horns. It had a parrot beak and a frill of bones on the back of its skull. Protoceratops was not very large, about six or eight feet long. However, over time, these dinosaurs grew larger. It was a plant-eater.

PROTOCERATOPS

March tempo

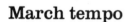

Trachodon (TRAK-o-don), nicknamed Rough Tooth, was a duckbilled dinosaur that ate underwater plants. On the upper and lower jaw it had two thousand teeth combined, which was more teeth than any other dinosaur. Trachodon had hollow air spaces in its skull to help breathe under water.

TRACHODON

Con moto